Potteries Operators
FLEET LIST

2nd. Edition

DAVID K. ROBERTS

£1

S

POTTERIES

OPERATORS

FLEET LIST

Second Edition
by
David K. Roberts

388 . 322 094246

Potteries Omnibus Preservation Society

1983

First published   1978
Second edition   1983

ISBN   0 9508788 0 4

Typeset & Printed by:
Counter Print, 3 Tipping Street, Stafford.   Tel: 41404

INTRODUCTION

This second 'Potteries Fleetlist' is an update of the first edition, which was published in 1978. The first Book's proceeds were put towards helping in the upkeep of the society's first bus, NEH 466. Since then, the society has acquired another ex. P.M.T. vehicle, 766 EVT, both of which are pictured on the front cover.

It is still possible to purchase the first fleetlist from the society so that the many changes that have occurred in the Potteries operators since 1978 can be seen.

ACKNOWLEDGEMENTS

The Author wishes to thank Bakers, Berresfords Motors Ltd., Copeland's Tours Ltd., Graham's Coaches, Pooles Coachways Ltd., The Potteries Motor Traction Co. Ltd., F. Proctor & Son Ltd., W. Stonier & Sons Ltd., Thompson's Tour and S. Turner & Sons Ltd. for their help and co-operation in compiling this fleetlist.

The Author would also like to thank Bakers of Biddulph, The Chester-field Bus Society, Mr. G. Durber and Mr. C.J. Smith for their photographic contributions.

Finally, thank you to you, the purchaser, for purchasing the publication.

MAY 1983   David K. Roberts
                           Longton, Stoke-on-Trent

THE FOLLOWING CODES ARE FOR BODYWORK TYPES IN THIS BOOK:—

Preceding the seating capacity figures -

B - Single-deck bus	C - Single-deck coach
DP- Single-deck dual-purpose vehicle	H - Double-deck highbridge bus

Seating capacity -
For double-deck vehicles, the upper deck capacity is given first,
e.g. 43/31 indicates 43 'over' 31

Following the seating capacity figures -

D - Front entrance/centre exit	F - Front entrance/exit
t - Toilet fitted	

FRONT COVER
No longer part of an operator's fleet, these buses are now preserved by the Potteries Omnibus Preservation Society. They are L466 (NEH 466), a Leyland 'Titian' OPD2, dating from 1949, now with a 1952 Northern Counties body; and 766 (766 EVT), an early Leyland 'Atlantean' PDR1/1, built in 1959 with a Weymann body. They are seen at the Sandwell transport rally in May 1979.

(C.J. Smith)

BAKER'S OF BIDDULPH
Congleton Road, Biddulph.

Chassis: Volvo B58-56
Built: 1973
Body: Plaxton C53F
ARE 999M   (To be re-registered but new number not known.)

Chassis: Volvo B58-56
Built: 1981
Body: Plaxton C53F
Ex. H. Wilson (Premier) of Stainforth
3275 RU (formerly RYG 169M)

Chassis: Volvo B58-56
Built: 1978
Body: Plaxton C57F
6106 RU (formerly XEH 1S)
5658 RU (formerly XEH 2S)

Chassis: Volvo B58-56
Built: 1978
Body: Plaxton C53F
9039 RU (formerly XEH 3S)
XEH 4S

Chassis: Ford Transit
Built: 1978
Body: Deansgate C12F
XEH 6S

Chassis: Ford Transit
Built: 1978
Body: Deansgate B12F
XEH 7S

Chassis: Volvo B58-56
Built: 1980
Body: Plaxton C55Ft
KRE 8V
KRE 9V (both to be re-registered)

Chassis: Volvo B58-56
Built: 1980
Body: Plaxton C53F
Ex. Astons of Kempsey in 1982
VAB 100V (to be re-registered)

Chassis: Volvo B10M-100
Built: 1982
Body: Plaxton C49Ft
XBF 1X (to be re-registered)

Chassis: Volvo B10M-100
Built: 1982
Body: Duple 'Goldliner' C42Ft
Ex. Parks of Hamilton, in 1983
FHS 735X
FHS 738X

Chassis: Volvo B10M-100
Built: 1983
Body: Plaxton C49F
8399 RU

4

BERRESFORD'S MOTORS LTD.
Cheddleton.

* denotes vehicles licensed to
Byrne Brothers, Buxton Road, Leek.

Chassis: Leyland 'Atlantean' PDR1/1
Built: 1964
Body: Weymann H43/31F
Ex. Bournemouth Transport in 1980
AEL 173B
AEL 178B

Chassis: Leyland 'Leopard' PSU4/3RT
Built: 1967
Body: Plaxton C43F
Ex. Jones Omnibus Services Ltd., Aberbeeg
in 1979
LWO 316E

Chassis: Leyland 'Leopard' PSU4/3R
Built: 1967
Body: Plaxton C40F
Ex. Trent Motor Traction Co. Ltd. in 1979
MRC 564E

Chassis: Leyland 'Atlantean' PDR1/3
Built: 1968
Body: Metro - Cammell H43/31F
Ex. West Yorkshire P.T.E. in 1980
LAK 289G

Chassis: Leyland 'Atlantean' PDR1/2
Built: 1968
Body: Northern Counties H44/33F
Ex. Merseyside P.T.E. in 1981
LCM 160G
LCM 161G

Chassis: Ford R192
Built: 1969
Body: Willowbrook B41F/B45F
respectively
Ex. Highland Omnibuses Ltd. in 1982
KST 360G
KST 367G

Chassis: Bristol LH6L
Built: 1970
Body: Northern Counties B39D
Ex. Smith, Waterhouses in 1982
* UTD 299H

Chassis: Leyland 'Leopard' PSU3/4R
Built: 1970
Body: Duple C48F
Ex. Maidstone & District Motor Services Ltd.
in 1981
VKN 627J

Chassis: A.E.C. 'Reliance' 6MU4R
Built: 1971
Body: Plaxton C45F
Ex. Direct Coal Co., Wetley Rocks in 1978
CYD 234J

Chassis: A.E.C. 'Reliance' 6MU4R
Built: 1971
Body: Willowbrook DP49F
Ex. Smith, Waterhouses in 1982
SWL 49J

Chassis: Bedford YRQ
Built: 1971
Body: Plaxton C45F
Ex. Direct Coal Co., in 1978
WNL 549J

Chassis: A.E.C. 'Swift' 2MP2R
Built: 1972
Body: Seddon B41D
Ex. Greater Manchester Transport in 1981
     TDK 543K
     TDK 544K
     TDK 545K

Chassis: A.E.C. 'Reliance' 6U2R
Built: 1972
Body: Park Royal DP45F
Ex. London Country Bus Services in 1980
     JPA 145K
     JPA 159K
     JPA 179K

Chassis: Bedford YRQ
Built: 1972
Body: Duple C45F
     LRE 649K
     LRE 650K

Chassis: Bedford CF
Built: 1972
Body: Deansgate 12 - seat
Ex. McCumesky, Stockport in 1975
     SXJ 112K

Chassis: Ford R1114
Built: 1973
Body: Duple C49F
Ex. Smith, Waterhouses in 1982
*   CNT 320L

Chassis: Bedford YRT
Built: 1973
Body: Duple C53F
Ex. Smith, Waterhouses in 1982
*   NTX 406L

Chassis: Bedford YRT
Built: 1973
Body: Plaxton C53F
     PRE 432L

Chassis: Bedford YRT
Built: 1973
Body: Plaxton C53F
*   RRF 232L
     URE 306L

Chassis: Ford R226
Built: 1974
Body: Duple C53F
Ex. Stubbs, Tunstall in 1978
     ONY 4M

Chassis: Leyland 'Leopard' PSU4B/4R
Built: 1974
Body: Plaxton C41F
Ex. British Airways in 1982
     WUL 264N

Chassis: Leyland 'Leopard' PSU3B/4R
Built: 1974
Body: Plaxton C51F
Ex. Lancashire United Transport in 1981
     XTB 748N
     XTB 749N

Chassis: Bedford CF
Built: 1977
Body: Bedford B12F
Ex. Brittain, Cheddleton (non-P.S.V.) in 1979
     TEH 853R
     TEH 870R

Chassis: Leyland 'Leopard' PSU3E/4R
Built: 1977/1978 respectively
Body: Plaxton C53F
     VVT 419S
     ENR 256T

COPELAND'S TOURS LTD.
Uttoxeter Road, Meir.

Chassis: Ford R226
Built: 1968
Body: Duple C53F
Ex. Hirst's Tours, Longton in 1978
    NFA 547G Lady Sarah II

Chassis: Ford R196
Built: 1969
Body: Plaxton C45F
Ex. Eastville, Bristol in 1977
    YBY 969G Lady Margaret II

Chassis: Ford R192
Built: 1971
Body: Plaxton C45F
Ex. Accrington Coachways; the future of
this vehicle was undecided when the fleet-
list was compiled.
    CTJ 71J

Chassis: Ford R1114
Built: 1974
Body: Duple C53F
    SVT 888N Lady Pamela II

Chassis: Ford R1114
Built: 1976
Body: Duple C53F
    NBF 743P Lady Ann

Chassis: Ford R1114
Built: 1977
Body: Plaxton C53F
    TRE 202R Lady Jubilee

Chassis: Ford R1114
Built: 1977
Body: Duple C53F
Ex. Blue Car, Nantwich in 1978
    UWD 812S Lady Brenda II

Chassis: Ford R1114
Built: 1978
Body: Plaxton C53F
Ex. Shearings, Altrincham in 1982
    WVM 551S Lady Jane II

Chassis: Peugeot 504
Built: 1978
Body: 7 - seat estate car
    XBF 253S

Chassis: Ford R1114
Built: 1979
Body: Plaxton C53F
    HBF 168V Wedgwood Lady

Chassis: Ford R1114
Built: 1979
Body: Duple C53F
Ex. Olsen, Medway in 1982
    JFD 287V Lady Elizabeth

Chassis: Ford R1114
Built: 1980
Body: Plaxton C53F
    KRE 440V Lady Linda II

Chassis: Ford R1114
Built: 1980
Body: Plaxton C53F
    ORF 888W Lady Diana

Chassis: Ford R1114
Built: 1983
Body: Plaxton C49F
    CVT 888Y Lady Christina III

GRAHAM'S COACHES
Newcastle Road, Talke.

Chassis: Ford R226
Built: 1966
Body: Plaxton C52F
Ex. Happy Days, Woodseaves in 1977
    KUD 339D

Chassis: Ford R192
Built: 1967
Body: Plaxton C45F
Ex. Smallwood, Leigh in 1981
    LNX 752E

Chassis: Ford R1014
Built: 1970
Body: Plaxton DP45F
Ex. Happy Days, Woodseaves in 1979
    CWU 186H

Chassis: Ford R1114
Built: 1973
Body: Duple C53F
Ex. Thompsons, Manchester in 1981
    TXD 696L

Chassis: Ford R1114
Built: 1974
Body: Duple C53F
Ex. Better Class Travel, Tean in 1982
    NSL 640M

Chassis: Ford R1114
Built: 1975
Body: Duple C53F
    LVT 976P

Chassis: Ford R1114
Built: 1978
Body: Plaxton C53F
    XBF 505S

Chassis: Ford R1114
Built: 1980
Body: Plaxton C53F
    KRE 114V

Chassis: Ford R1114
Built: 1981
Body: Plaxton C53F
    PRF 469W

Chassis: Leyland 'Leopard' PSU3E/4R
Built: 1982
Body: Plaxton C57F/C53F respectively
    VVT 576X
    VVT 577X

Chassis: Volvo B10M-100
Built: 1983
Body: Plaxton C57F
    YUT 628Y

POOLE'S COACHWAYS LTD.
High Street, Alsagers Bank.

Chassis: A.E.C. 'Reliance' 2U3RA
Built: 1967
Body: Willowbrook DP49F
          DRF 133E

Chassis: Leyland 'Leopard' PSU3A/4R
Built: 1969
Body: Plaxton C49F
Ex. City of Oxford Motor Services in 1980
          HRN 957G

Chassis: Leyland 'Leopard' PSU3B/4R
Built: 1972
Body: Plaxton C53F
Ex. Barton Transport Ltd. in 1977
          LAL 318K

Chassis: Leyland 'Leopard' PSU4B/2R
Built: 1972
Body: Pennine B47F
Ex. Lancaster City Council in 1981
          NTD 117K

Chassis: Leyland 'Leopard' PSU3B/4R
Built: 1972
Body: Willowbrook DP49F
          NRE 582L

Chassis: Leyland 'Leopard' PSU3B/4R
Built: 1972
Body: Plaxton DP51F
Ex. West Wales Motors Ltd., Tycroes in 1982
          VBX 222L

Chassis: Leyland 'Leopard' PSU3B/4R
Built: 1973
Body: Willowbrook B53F
          RBF 987M

Chassis: Leyland 'Leopard' PSU3B/4R
Built: 1975
Body: Willowbrook B55F
          LBF 796P

Chassis: Leyland 'Leopard' PSU3B/4R
Built: 1978
Body: Marshall DP53F
          XFA 967S

THE POTTERIES MOTOR TRACTION CO. LTD.

Depots at:- **Burslem (b)**
            Cheadle (c)
            Hanley (h)
            Newcastle-under-Lyme (n)

Chassis: Leyland 'Leopard' PSU3E/4R
Built: 1978 - 1981
Body: (19) Duple C47F
          (20/21) Duple C46F
          (22) Willowbrook C47F
19n URF 19S   21n GRF 221V
20h XBF 20S   22h OEH 22W

Chassis: Leyland 'Tiger'
Body: Plaxton
Built: 1983
Body: Plaxton 'Paramount' C--F
23 ERF - - - Y   24 ERF - - - Y
At present on order. To be delivered later in 1983

Chassis: Leyland 'Leopard' PSU3B/4R
Built: 1974
Body: Duple C46F
45n SEH 272M   47h SEH 274N
46b SEH 273N   48h SEH 275N

Chassis: Leyland 'Leopard' PSU3E/4R
Built: 1978 - 1982
Body: (52-63) Duple C49F
          (64-68) Duple C53F
          (69-71) Willowbrook C49F

52n URF 52S   62h XBF 62S
53b XBF 53S   63b XBF 63S
54n XBF 54S   64n GRF 264V
55n XBF 55S   65h GRF 265V
56h XBF 56S   66h GRF 266V
57h XBF 57S   67b GRF 267V
58n XBF 58S   68b GRF 268V
59n XBF 59S   69b VFA 69X
60n XBF 60S   70b VFA 70X
61h XBF 61S   71b VFA 71X

Chassis: Leyland 'Tiger'
Built: 1983
Body: Plaxton 'Paramount' C--F
72 ERF - - - Y   74 ERF - - - Y
73 ERF - - - Y
At present on order. To be delivered later in 1983

Chassis: Austin FL2DR
Built: 1982
Body: Carbodies 7 - seater
101n XRF 1X   102n XRF 2X

Chassis: Mercedes-Benz 207D/307D resp.
Built: 1982/1983 respectively
Body: Whittaker/Reeves Burgess
          12 - seaters respectively
110h YRE 470Y 111h YRE 471Y

Chassis : Bristol RELL
Built: 1968
Body: ECW B53F
Ex. Bristol Omnibus Company, 1983
170 MAE 154F   173 OHU 766F
171 MHW 847F   174 OHU 769F
172 NHU 197F
Taken into P.M.T. stock, May 1983. Allocations not known at the time of printing.

A Volvo B10M with Plaxton 'Viewmaster' bodywork of Bakers of Biddulph.
This coach is fitted with a Video/T.V., rear galley and toilet facility.
(Bakers of Biddulph

Formerly with Highland Omnibuses and now with Berresford's of
Cheddleton, KST 367G, a Ford R192 with a Willowbrook body
is seen at Hanley Bus Station in December 1982.
(C.J. Smith

Three examples of Berresford's fleet seen at their Cheddleton garage. They are (left to right) LWO 316E, a Leyland 'Leopard' with Plaxton body; URE 306L, a Bedford YRT with Plaxton body and JPA 145K, an A.E.C. 'Reliance' with Park Royal body, now with a Willowbrook front.

(Chesterfield Bus Society

"One of Copelands" - "Lady Elizabeth" (JFD 287V) keeps company with "Lady Linda II" (KRE 440V) at the company's garage at Meir in December 1982.

(C.J. Smith

Delivered in 1981, Copeland's Tours Ford R1114 (ORF 888W)
with Plaxton bodywork is appropriately named "Lady Diana".
(C.J. Smith

Graham's Coaches VVT 577X, a Leyland 'Leopard' PSU3E/4R,
stands outside its former depot at Sandyford, Tunstall on a fine
afternoon in August 1982.

(D.K. Roberts

Possibly the finest 'decker' in the Potteries!
RWC 944D, a Bristol FLF6G/E.C.W. of Graham's Coaches, was immaculate
mechanically and structurally, as seen outside its former depot at Sandyford.
It has now been sold.

(G. Durber

XFA 967S is a Leyland 'Leopard' with rare Marshall "Camair" body of the Poole's Coachways fleet at Newcastle Bus Station in 1979.
(C.J. Smith

One of only three in the P.M.T. fleet is this Bristol RELH with ECW body with coach seats. 210 (MVT 210K) is seen in the High Street in Stone, having arrived from Longton on service 93 in 1976.
(C.J. Smith

P.M.T. buses at Hanley Depot in December 1982. They are (left to right): Leyland 'National', 233 (PVT 233L); Leyland 'Titian' OPD2, L466 (NEH 466) and now owned by the Potteries Omnibus Preservation Society; Bristol VRTSL6L/E.C.W. 706 (GRF 706V); Bristol VRTSL6G/ E.C.W. 620 (GBF 76N); Daimler 'Fleetline' CRG6LX, formerly L1035 and now in the training fleet as T1 (AEH 135C) and Leyland 'Leopard' 47 (SEH 274N).

(C.J. Smith)

Procter's Leyland "Tiger", WFA 210X at the depot at Fenton
in December 1982.

(C.J. Smith

Stoniers A.E.C. 'Swift' TDK 546K is seen in Old Hall Street, Hanley, on
the 66 service to Meir.

(Chesterfield Bus Society

Formerly London Transport No. DMS 2164 - OJD 164R is now No. 6 in the Turner's of Brown Edge fleet. The location is Hanley bus station in August 1982, shortly after delivery to Turner's which explains the absence of destination blinds. The vehicle is a Daimler Fleetline FE30GR with Park Royal bodywork.

(D.K. Roberts

Thompson's Tours D.A.F./Jonckherre executive YRF 754Y is seen at their Trentham depot in December 1982.

(C.J. Smith

18

Chassis: Bristol RESL6L
Built: 1972
Body: ECW B44F

204n	PVT 204L	207n	PVT 207L

Chassis: Bristol RELH6L
Built: 1971
Body: ECW DP49F

210c	MVT 210K	211c	MVT 211K
212c	MVT 212K		

Chassis: Bristol RELL6L
Built: 1972/1973
Body: ECW B53F

215b	PVT 215L	223b	PVT 223L
216n	PVT 216L	224b	PVT 224L
217n	PVT 217L	225b	PVT 225L
218n	PVT 218L	226b	PVT 226L
219b	PVT 219L	227n	PVT 227L
220n	PVT 220L	228n	PVT 228L
221n	PVT 221L	229n	PVT 229L
222n	PVT 222L		

Chassis: Leyland 'National' 1151/1R integral-construction vehicles
Built: 1972/1973
Body: B52F

230h	PVT 230L	238n	PVT 238L
231h	PVT 231L	240h	PVT 240L
232h	PVT 232L	241h	PVT 241L
233h	PVT 233L	242h	PVT 242L
234h	PVT 234L	243h	PVT 243L
235h	PVT 235L	244h	PVT 244L
236n	PVT 236L	245h	PVT 245L
237n	PVT 237L	246h	PVT 246L

Chassis: Leyland 'National' 1051/1R integral-construction vehicles
Built: 1973/1974
Body: B41F

247h	XEH 247M	255c	XEH 255M
248h	XEH 248M	256c	XEH 256M
249h	XEH 249M	257c	XEH 257M
250h	XEH 250M	258c	XEH 258M
251h	XEH 251M	259c	XEH 259M
252h	XEH 252M	260c	XEH 260M
253c	XEH 253M	261c	XEH 261M
254c	XEH 254M		

Chassis: Leyland 'National' 11351/1R integral-construction vehicles
Built: 1974 - 1976
Body: B52F

262n	PEH 262M	276n	KRE 276P
263n	PEH 263M	277n	KRE 277P
264n	PEH 264M	278n	KRE 278P
265n	PEH 265M	279n	KRE 279P
266h	PEH 266M	280h	KRE 280P
267h	GBF 70N	281h	KRE 281P
268h	GBF 71N	282h	KRE 282P
269h	GBF 72N	283h	KRE 283P
270n	GBF 73N	284h	KRE 284P
271n	GBF 74N	285h	KRE 285P

Chassis: Leyland 'National' 11351A/1R integral-construction vehicles
Built: 1977
Body: B52F

286n	SFA 286R	287n	SFA 287R

Chassis: Bristol VRTSL6L
Built: 1978
Body: ECW H43/31F

600n	YBF 686S

Chassis: Bristol VRTSL6G
Built: 1974/1975
Body: ECW H43/31F

601b	OEH 601M	616b	REH 816M
602b	OEH 602M	617n	REH 817M
603b	OEH 603M	618b	REH 818M
604b	OEH 604M	619b	GBF 75N
605h	OEH 605M	620h	GBF 76N
606h	OEH 606M	621h	GBF 77N
607n	OEH 607M	622n	GBF 78N
608b	OVT 608M	623h	GBF 79N
609b	OVT 609M	624n	GBF 80N
610n	REH 810M	625h	GBF 81N
611h	REH 811M	626b	HRE 526N
612n	REH 812M	627h	HRE 527N
613n	REH 813M	629h	HRE 529N
614n	REH 814M	631n	HRE 531N
615b	REH 815M		

Chassis: Bristol VRTSL6L
Built: 1975 - 1979
Body: ECW H43/31F
661 & 662 were ex Ribble Motor Services Ltd. in 1982. 663-5 were ex National Welsh in 1978

632b	KRE 632P	640h	KRE 640P
633h	KRE 633P	641b	KRE 641P
634n	KRE 634P	642n	KRE 642P
635h	KRE 635P	643n	KRE 643P
636h	KRE 636P	644h	OFA 644P
637h	KRE 637P	645h	OFA 645P
638h	KRE 638P	646h	OFA 646P
639h	KRE 639P	647h	OFA 647P

648b	PEH 648R	674n	URF 674S
649b	PEH 649R	675b	URF 675S
650b	PEH 650R	676b	URF 676S
651n	PEH 651R	677b	URF 677S
652n	PEH 652R	678h	YBF 678S
653n	PEH 653R	679h	YBF 679S
654h	PEH 654R	680h	YBF 680S
655n	PEH 655R	681h	YBF 681S
656h	PEH 656R	682b	YBF 682S
657h	PEH 657R	683n	YBF 683S
658n	URF 658S	684n	YBF 684S
659n	URF 659S	685h	YBF 685S
660n	URF 660S	687h	YBF 687S
661h	CBV 3S	688n	BRF 688T
662b	CBV 4S	689b	BRF 689T
663b	SKG 897S	690h	BRF 690T
664b	SKG 902S	691b	BRF 691T
665b	SKG 903S	692h	BRF 692T
666b	URF 666S	693h	BRF 693T
667h	URF 667S	694n	GRF 694V
668n	URF 668S	695h	GRF 695V
669b	URF 669S	696n	GRF 696V
670b	URF 670S	697n	GRF 697V
671n	URF 671S	698n	GRF 698V
672h	URF 672S	699n	GRF 699V
673n	URF 673S		

Chassis: Dennis 'Dominator' DD102
Built: 1978
Body: Alexander H43/31F
700n   XBF 700S

Chassis: Bristol VRTSL6L
Built: 1979/1980
Body: ECW H43/31F

701h	GRF 701V	717n	MFA 717V
702h	GRF 702V	718n	MFA 718V
703n	GRF 703V	719b	MFA 719V
704n	GRF 704V	720c	MFA 720V
705h	GRF 705V	721c	MFA 721V
706h	GRF 706V	722h	MFA 722V
707c	GRF 707V	723b	MFA 723V
708h	GRF 708V	724b	NEH 724W
709h	GRF 709V	725b	NEH 725W
710h	GRF 710V	726c	NEH 726W
711b	GRF 711V	727b	NEH 727W
712b	GRF 712V	728b	NEH 728W
713h	GRF 713V	729h	NEH 729W
714c	GRF 714V	730n	NEH 730W
715c	GRF 715V	731h	NEH 731W
716n	GRF 716V	732n	NEH 732W

Chassis: Foden semi-integral vehicle
Built: 1978
Body: Northern Counties H43/31F
           900   WVT 900S
De-licenced and stored, May 1983

P.M.T. DRIVER TRAINING VEHICLES
Chassis: Daimler 'Fleetline' CRG6LX
Built: 1965
Body: Alexander H41/31F
           T1   AEH 135C

Chassis: Leyland 'Leopard' PSU4A/4R
Built: 1968
Body: Marshall B43F
           T3   TVT 128G

F. PROCTOR & SON LTD.
Dewsbury Road, Fenton.

Chassis: Bedford VAS5
Built: 1974
Body: Duple C29F
Ex. Whittle Group in 1976
      PUX 706M

Chassis: Leyland 'Atlantean' AN68/1R
Built: 1974
Body: Alexander H45/31F
      GBF 278N
      GBF 279N

Chassis: Bristol LH6L
Built: 1975
Body: Plaxton C43F
Ex. North Staffs. Motors in 1980
      JRB 519N

Chassis: Leyland 'Leopard' PSU5A/4R
Built: 1975
Body: Duple C57F
Ex. Mosley, Barugh Green in 1978
      JKY 944P
      JKY 945P

Chassis: A.E.C. 'Reliance' 6U3ZR
Built: 1975
Body: Duple C57F
      LEH 164P

Chassis: Bristol VRTLL6G
Built: 1976
Body: Alexander H49/34D
Ex. Tayside Regional Council in 1981
      OSR 204R

Chassis: Bedford YMT
Built: 1977
Body: Plaxton C53F
      RVT 1R

Chassis: Bedford YLQ
Built: 1977
Body: Duple C45F
      TFA 348R

Chassis: A.E.C. 'Reliance' 6U3ZR
Built: 1977/1978 respectively
Body: Duple C57F
      UFA 698R
      AFA 729S

Chassis: Bristol LH6L
Built: 1979
Body: Plaxton C45F
Ex. Jalna Coaches, Church Gresley in 1981
      YUT 326T

Chassis: Leyland 'Leopard' PSU3E/4R
Built: 1979
Body: Plaxton C45F
Ex. Glenton Tours, London in 1981
      AJD 166T

Chassis: Leyland 'Leopard' PSU3E/4R
Built: 1980
Body: Plaxton C53F
      HRE 128V
      HRE 129V

Chassis: Leyland 'Leopard' PSU3E/4R
Built: 1980
Body: Plaxton C53F
Ex. Middleton, Rugeley in 1981
           JRE 355V

Chassis: Leyland 'Leopard' PSU5C/4R
Built: 1981
Body: Duple C44F
           OEH 930W

Chassis: Leyland 'Tiger' TRCTL11/3R
Built: 1982
Body: Duple C57F
           WFA 209X
           WFA 210X

Chassis: Leyland 'Leopard' PSU5C/4R
Built: 1982
Body: Plaxton C53F
           WVT 107X

Chassis: Leyland 'Tiger' TRCTL11/3R
Built: 1982
Body: Duple C36Ft
           ARE 508Y

Chassis: Leyland 'Tiger' TRCTL11/3R
Built: 1983
Body: Plaxton C49Ft
           DVT 994Y

W. STONIER & SONS LTD.
Parsonage Street, Tunstall.

Chassis: Leyland 'Atlantean' PDR1/1
Built: 1964
Body: Weymann H43/31F
Ex. Bournemouth Transport in 1980
AEL 172B

Chassis: Bedford VAM14
Built: 1967
Body: Duple C45F
Ex. Williams, Treorchy in 1971
MTX 500E

Chassis: Leyland 'Atlantean' PDR1/3
Built: 1968
Body: Metro - Cammell H43/31F
Ex. West Yorkshire P.T.E. in 1980
LAK 296G
LAK 292G

Chassis: Daimler 'Fleetline' CRG6LX
Built: 1969
Body: Northern Counties H44/33F
Ex. Turner, Brown Edge in 1979
TRF 172G

Chassis: A.E.C. 'Swift' 2MP2R
Built: 1971/1972
Body: Seddon B41D
Ex. Greater Manchester Transport in 1980
TDK 541J
TDK 542K
TDK 546K

Chassis: A.E.C. 'Reliance' 6U2R
Built: 1972
Body: Park Royal DP45F
Ex. London Country Bus Services in 1980
JPA 176K
JPA 181K

Chassis: Ford R226
Built: 1972
Body: Plaxton C53F
Ex. Stubbs, Tunstall in 1978
LWP 670K

Chassis: Leyland 'Atlantean' AN68/
Built: 1972
Body: Northern Counties H45/31
Ex. Maidstone Borough Council in 1977
EKR 153L
EKR 154L

Chassis: Bedford YRT
Built: 1973
Body: Duple C45F
NEH 261M

Chassis: Bedford YRT
Built: 1974
Body: Plaxton C45F
RVT 331M

Chassis: Leyland 'Leopard' PSU3C/4
Built: 1975
Body: Duple C45F
LBF 248P

Chassis: Leyland 'Leopard' PSU3E/4
Built: 1977
Body: Plaxton C53F
TVT 863R

Chassis: Leyland 'Leopard' PSU3E/4
Built: 1978
Body: Plaxton C53F
XBF 155S

THOMPSON'S TOURS
New Park Garage, Trentham.

Chassis: A.E.C. 'Reliance' 6U3ZR
Built: 1974
Body: Plaxton C34C
Ex. Glenton Tours, London in 1981
   TME 133M
   GYT 146N

Chassis: Ford R1114
Built: 1977
Body: Plaxton C53F
Ex. Sharrock, Bolton in 1980
   RBN 217S
   RBN 218S

Chassis: Ford R1114
Built: 1982
Body: Duple C53F
   XFA 749X

Chassis: Mercedes-Benz 307D
Built: 1982
Body: Devon C12F
   XFA 750X

Chassis: Ford R1114
Built: 1982
Body: Duple C53F
   YRF 751Y
   YRF 752Y
   YRF 753Y

Chassis: DAF MB200DKTL600
Built: 1982
Body: Jonckherre C44Ft
   YRF 754Y

Chassis: A.E.C. 'Reliance' 6MU4R
Built: 1976
Body: Plaxton C34C
Ex. Glenton Tours Ltd., London
   LYH 150P

S. TURNER & SONS LTD.
High Lane, Brown Edge.

Chassis: A.E.C. 'Reliance' 6U3ZR
Built: 1974
Body: Duple C53F
       TBF 873M

Chassis: Daimler 'Fleetline' CRL6
Built: 1975
Body: Northern Counties H44/33F
     10   JBF 169N

Chassis: Daimler 'Fleetline' FE30GR
Built: 1977
Body: Park Royal H44/29F
Ex. London Transport in 1982
     5 OJD 128R
     6 OJD 164R

Chassis: Bedford YMT
Built: 1977
Body: Duple C53F
Ex. Limebourne, London in 1978
     TMJ 633R

Chassis: Leyland 'Fleetline' FE30AGR
Built: 1978
Body: Northern Counties H44/33F
     9 AFA 489S

Chassis: A.E.C. 'Reliance' 6u3ZR
Built: 1978
Body: Plaxton C53F
Ex. Gardiner, Spennymore in 1978
     APT 843S

Chassis: Leyland 'Fleetline' FE30AC
Built: 1980
Body: Northern Counties H44/33
     8 LVT 699V

Chassis: Leyland 'Tiger' TRCTL11/
Built: 1982
Body: Plaxton C53F
     WBF 718X

26

"NOTES"

"NOTES"

ISBN 0 950 8788 0 4